STAR WARS®

THE HUNT FOR AURRA SING

STAR WARS®

THE HUNT FOR AURRA SING

script
TIM TRUMAN

pencils
DAVIDÉ FABBRI

inks
CHRISTIAN DALLA VECCHIA

colors
DAVE McCAIG

letters
STEVE DUTRO

collection cover artist
ANDREW ROBINSON

DARK HORSE COMICS®

publisher
MIKE RICHARDSON

editor
DAVE LAND

assistant editor
PHILIP SIMON

collection designer
LANI SCHREIBSTEIN

art director
MARK COX

Special thanks to CHRIS CERASI
and LUCY AUTREY WILSON at Lucas Licensing

STAR WARS®: THE HUNT FOR AURRA SING

This book collects issues 28 through 31 of the Dark Horse comic-
book series *Star Wars*®

Published by
Dark Horse Comics, Inc.
10956 SE Main Street
Milwaukie, OR 97222

www.darkhorse.com

Comic Shop Locator Service: (888) 266-4226

First edition: July 2002
ISBN: 1-56971-651-X

10 9 8 7 6 5 4 3 2 1

PRINTED IN CHINA

CORUSCANT--CAPITAL PLANET OF THE REPUBLIC.

PEERCE! WHAT HAVE YOU FOUND?

BLOOD!

THEN WE'VE PICKED UP HER TRAIL AGAIN!

PEERCE WOULD SAY THAT THIS IS A CERTAINTY, YES!

SHE IS CLOSE, J'MIKEL! THE BLOOD IS STILL WARM! BESIDES-- PEERCE CAN FEEL HER! SHE CLOAKS HER PRESENCE WELL! BUT SHE IS OUT THERE-- SOMEWHERE!

YES, SHE IS STRONG, THIS ONE.

THE BLOOD MASTERS-- IS IT HERS?

PERHAPS. BUT PEERCE IS THINKING MORE SO THAT IT IS NOT!

COULD OUR INFORMANT BE RIGHT? COULD IT REALLY BE HER?

WHO CAN SAY, MY YOUNG PADÁWAN? MOST SAY THAT SHE'S A MYTH, NOTHING MORE.

IF SHE ISN'T, SURELY SHE'D NOT SHOW HERSELF ON CORUSCANT, IN THE VERY HEART OF THE REPUBLIC!

PEERCE IS THINKING THAT SHE IS REAL, ALL RIGHT...

...THAT MUCH IS VERY CLEAR!

A SQUAD OF REPUBLIC PEACE OFFICERS!

AYE. BUT SQUADS ARE ALWAYS MANNED BY FIVE. PEERCE SEES ONLY FOUR BODIES HERE!

SEE? ONE GAVE CHASE TO THE VILLAIN!

YES, MY FRIEND-- OR WAS PURSUED!

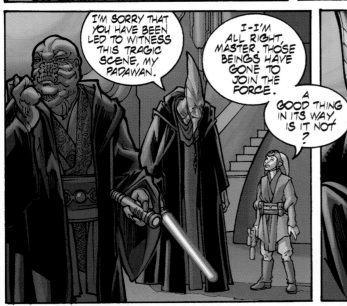

I'M SORRY THAT YOU HAVE BEEN LED TO WITNESS THIS TRAGIC SCENE, MY PADAWAN.

I-I'M ALL RIGHT, MASTER. THOSE BEINGS HAVE GONE TO JOIN THE FORCE.

A GOOD THING IN ITS WAY, IS IT NOT?

YOU ARE A WISE STUDENT--AND BRAVE. YOUR WORDS GIRD THE HEART OF AN OLD JEDI.

SOMEDAY, YOU WILL BE A GREAT KNIGHT.

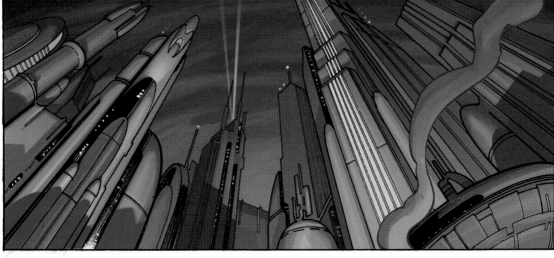

CAREFUL, CHILD. THERE IS A BLIND ALLEY JUST AHEAD! OUR QUARRY MUST BE HERE!

MASTER! THAT SMELL...

IONIZED AIR--CHARGED BY A LIGHTSABER DUEL!

LOOK!

PEERCE! MY FRIEND! WHAT HAS HAPPENED HERE?

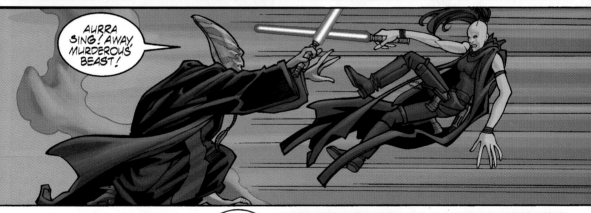

AH, A PADAWAN. HOW NICE.

DON'T WORRY, LITTLE FOOL, YOUR MASTER HAS JOINED THE FORCE.

IT'S A GOOD THING, IN ITS WAY.

IS IT NOT?

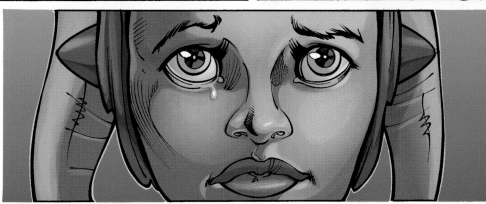

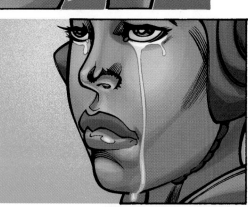

MORNING. THE COUNCIL CHAMBER OF THE JEDI TEMPLE.

TWO JEDI, SLAIN ON CORUSCANT ITSELF?

YES, MASTER PIELL-- WITHIN THE VERY SHADOWS OF THE TEMPLE.

AND WHAT OF THE PADAWAN?

SHE IS IN THE CARE OF OUR PHYSICIANS. IT WILL TAKE MANY MONTHS TO FREE HER MIND OF THE HORROR SHE'S WITNESSED.

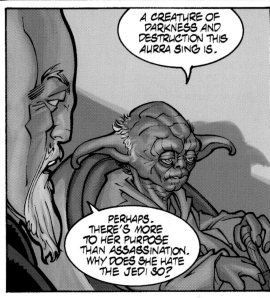

A CREATURE OF DARKNESS AND DESTRUCTION THIS AURRA SING IS.

PERHAPS. THERE'S MORE TO HER PURPOSE THAN ASSASSINATION. WHY DOES SHE HATE THE JEDI SO?

AND HOW DID SHE BECOME SO STRONG? SHE CUT DOWN TWO JEDI AND A SQUAD OF REPUBLIC PEACE OFFICERS!

TRULY, HER POWERS ARE GREAT. THE DARK SIDE MUST BE STRONG IN HER.

NO--NOT YET. I MET HER, REMEMBER--ON TATOOINE. I DON'T KNOW WHY, OR HOW, BUT SHE IS NEITHER A DISCIPLE OF THE LIGHT OR THE DARK.

SHE IS SOME-WHERE IN BETWEEN. AN ASSASSIN, PERHAPS...

...BUT NOT A RANDOM MURDERER.

BUT A KILLER, NONETHELESS!

DARK WOMAN, YOU WERE NOT ASKED TO ATTEND THIS MEETING.

YOU KNEW THAT I WOULD COME, MASTER WINDU. HOW COULD I NOT?

I WILL TRACK THIS CREATURE NAMED AURRA SING, AND END THE HORROR THAT RIDES HER SHADOW!

YOU WILL NOT.

WE ALL KNOW WHAT HAPPENED WHILE SHE WAS IN YOUR CARE. SHE WAS YOUR STUDENT--BUT HER FAILINGS ARE NOT YOURS. OF THAT WE'RE SURE.

THEN YOU ARE MORE CERTAIN THAN I.

ALL THE MORE REASON FOR YOU NOT TO FOLLOW HER.

IF YOU FACE HER, MANY FEELINGS WILL GUIDE YOUR WEAPON...REMORSE...UNCERTAINTY...A DESIRE TO STILL A VOICE THAT TELLS YOU THAT YOU FAILED HER...THE JEDI ORDER...YOURSELF.

AURRA SING IS A GHOST THAT HAS HAUNTED YOU FOR TOO LONG.

I MUST STAND BY THE SENIOR COUNCILOR'S RULING.

HOWEVER, I VOLUNTEER TO GO IN MY FIRST TEACHER'S STEAD.

AND I, MASTERS.

FOR THE BOY TO GO, IS IT WISE? KILLED THE LAD'S FATHER DID THIS AURRA SING.

I DO NOT SEEK VENGEANCE. I SEEK JUSTICE.

AURRA SING HAS KILLED JEDI. SHE WILL KILL MORE IF SHE IS NOT STOPPED.

EASY TO SPEAK NOW, ARE THESE WORDS. SAY THE SAME, WOULD YOU, IF CROSSING LIGHTSABERS WITH HER, YOU WERE? FEEL THE SAME, WOULD YOU, IF INTO HER EYES YOU WERE LOOKING?

WITH ALL DUE RESPECT, MASTER, IF YOU THINK THAT MY WORDS COME EASILY, YOU ARE WRONG.

I HAVE SEARCHED MY HEART. THE WISH FOR REVENGE DOES NOT MOTIVATE ME.

HOW CAN YOU BE SURE, PADAWAN HETT?

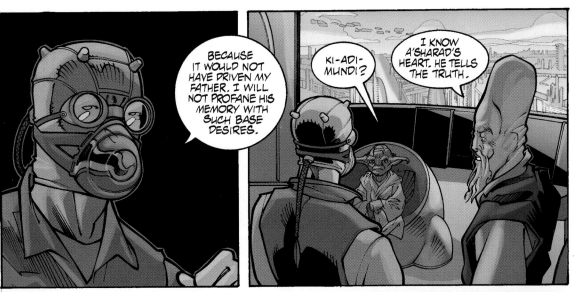

BECAUSE IT WOULD NOT HAVE DRIVEN MY FATHER. I WILL NOT PROFANE HIS MEMORY WITH SUCH BASE DESIRES.

KI-ADI-MUNDI?

I KNOW A'SHARAD'S HEART. HE TELLS THE TRUTH.

I HOPE YOU ARE RIGHT, MY FRIEND. IF YOU AREN'T, THE ARMS OF THE DARK SIDE WILL BE THROWN WIDE TO WELCOME THE BOY.

I'LL NOT ALLOW THAT TO HAPPEN. MASTER SHARAD HETT ENTRUSTED ME WITH TEACHING HIS SON. I'LL REMAIN WORTHY OF THAT TRUST.

THAT WHICH WE INTEND IS NOT ALWAYS WHAT HAPPENS, KI. REMEMBER THAT.

IT IS A LESSON THAT I, MYSELF, LEARNED ONLY TOO WELL!

SO BE IT, KI-ADI-MUNDI. THE CHARGE IS YOURS. AURRA SING HAS NO DOUBT FLED. A CRUISER WILL BE PREPARED FOR YOU.

IT'S SAID THAT THE FEMALE IS THE DEADLIEST IN ANY SPECIES, MASTER MUNDI. BEARING THAT IN MIND, PERHAPS WE SHOULD MAKE THIS MATCH MORE EVEN. I, TOO, SHALL GO!

A GOOD IDEA, ADI GALLIA-- AS MUCH FOR YOUR MASTERY OF DIPLOMACY AS FOR YOUR ABILITY WITH THE LIGHT-SABER.

THE COUNCIL GIVES YOU ITS LEAVE, MY FRIENDS. FIND THIS ASSASSIN AND STOP HER.

MAY THE FORCE BE WITH YOU.

THE PLANET TALAS, IN THE KAMDON SYSTEM.

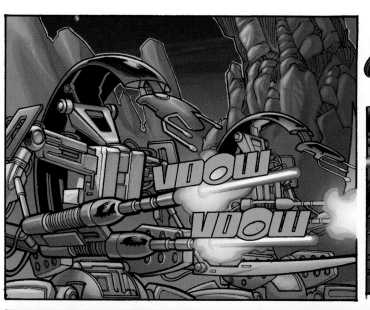

BOOM

NO!
NO!

IT WAS ONLY A TEST!

I DON'T LIKE TESTS!

NONETHELESS, WE HAD TO BE SURE!

YES! SURE THAT YOU'RE AS GOOD AS THE STORIES SAY YOU ARE! IF WE WANTED TO KILL YOU, THE DROIDEKAS WOULD HAVE BEEN SHIELDED.

AN EXPENSIVE TRIAL. YOU MUST HAVE PAID THE COLICOIDS WELL.

WITH THE MONEY YOU PAID FOR THOSE *DROIDEKAS*, YOU COULD HAVE BOUGHT A PLANET!

WE ALREADY HAVE ONE OF THOSE! YOU'RE STANDING ON IT!

ALTHOUGH OUR RELOCATION HERE WAS THROUGH NO CHOICE OF OUR OWN!

IT'S BEEN A LONG TIME SINCE WE TASTED THE SWEET WATERS OF OUR *MON CALAMARI* HOMEWORLD.

WE MISS IT SO.

TOUCHING. HOWEVER, I'M HERE FOR YOUR MONEY, NOT TO LISTEN TO YOUR SIMPERING.

WHY HAVE YOU SUMMONED ME?

I AM *TALLET*, AND THIS IS MY EGG-MATE *LEKKET*.

ONCE, WE WERE HONORED CITIZENS OF THE FLOATING CITY OF *HEURKEA*...

...AND THE MOST PROSPEROUS QUARREN IN THE CALAMARI SYSTEM!

"WITH THE GUARDSMEN WAS A *JEDI!*"

"TO ESCAPE CAPTURE, LEKKET AND I FLED THROUGH OUR FACTORY! THE JEDI PURSUED US!"

"YES--AND THAT'S WHEN *THE DISASTER* HAPPENED!"

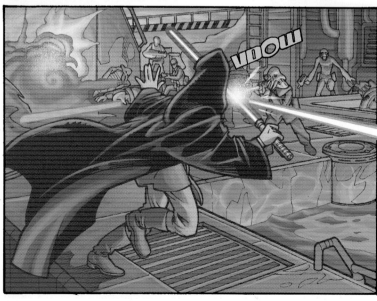

VDOW

TOONK

SSSSH

GAHH

"THE JEDI CAUSED A BLASTER BOLT TO PENETRATE A TOXIC *FUEL CELL!* MY POOR *TALLET* WAS CAUGHT IN THE FLOW, AND THE *ACID-LIKE* FUEL SEARED HIS FLESH!"

"OUR FLIGHT WAS HIDDEN BY THE VILE CHEMICAL CLOUD. I PULLED MY BELOVED, PAIN-WRACKED EGG-MATE TO SAFETY!"

"BOARDING A HIDDEN ESCAPE CRUISER, WE FLED MON CALAMARI FOREVER!"

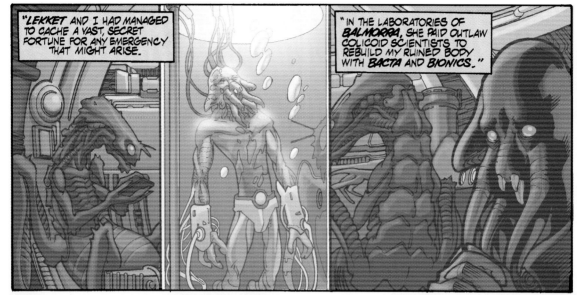

"*LEKKET* AND I HAD MANAGED TO CACHE A VAST, SECRET FORTUNE FOR ANY EMERGENCY THAT MIGHT ARISE.

"IN THE LABORATORIES OF *BALMORRA*, SHE PAID OUTLAW COLICOID SCIENTISTS TO REBUILD MY RUINED BODY WITH *BACTA* AND *BIONICS*."

WHEN TALLET WAS ABLE TO TRAVEL AGAIN, WE FLED THE SYSTEM AND BOUGHT THIS HORRID PLANET.

WE HAVE HIDDEN HERE EVER SINCE, DREAMING OF REVENGE.

REVENGE. AND I AM YOUR *INSTRUMENT* FOR THIS?

THINK AGAIN, I'M A *BOUNTY HUNTER*. AN *AVENGER*-- BUT NOT A MERE PAID ASSASSIN.

IT IS RUMORED THAT YOU HAVE SLAIN *JEDI*. IS THIS TRUE?

EVERY RUMOR HOLDS GRAINS OF TRUTH. OR SO I'VE HEARD.

IT HAS TAKEN US A LONG TIME, BUT WE HAVE FOUND THE JEDI WHO HELPED TIKKES RUIN US--THE JEDI WHO DID *THIS* TO ME!

WE WOULD *ENJOY* HER DEATH. WE THINK THAT *YOU* WOULD ENJOY IT, *TOO.*

PERHAPS. I'M EASILY ENTERTAINED.

WHO *IS* THIS JEDI? WHERE MIGHT I FIND HER?

SHE IS A *STRANGE* ONE-- EVEN AMONG THE JEDI. HER DEVOTION TO THE FORCE IS SUCH THAT SHE EVEN RENOUNCED HER OWN NAME AS A SIGN OF HER SELFLESS FEALITY.

SHE IS KNOWN ONLY AS...

...THE *DARK WOMAN!*

THE DARK WOMAN.

WHO COULD BELIEVE IT? AFTER ALL THESE YEARS. ALL MY SEARCHING.

NOW, YOU FALL RIGHT INTO MY LAP.

THE DARK WOMAN.

JEDI. TEACHER.

ENEMY.

TOMORROW, I WILL KNOW JOY. REAL JOY. FOR THE FIRST TIME IN MY LIFE.

TOMORROW...

...YOU DIE.

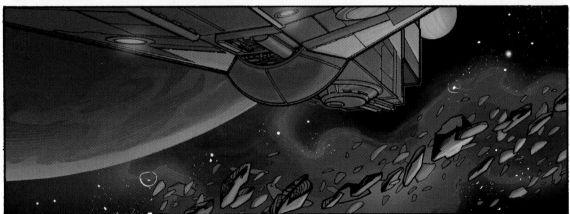

THERE SHE IS! OUR SCOUTS TRAILED HER WELL!

THEN LET'S GET THIS OVER WITH.

TAKE HER, BEFORE SHE DISAPPEARS INTO THE ASTEROID BELT.

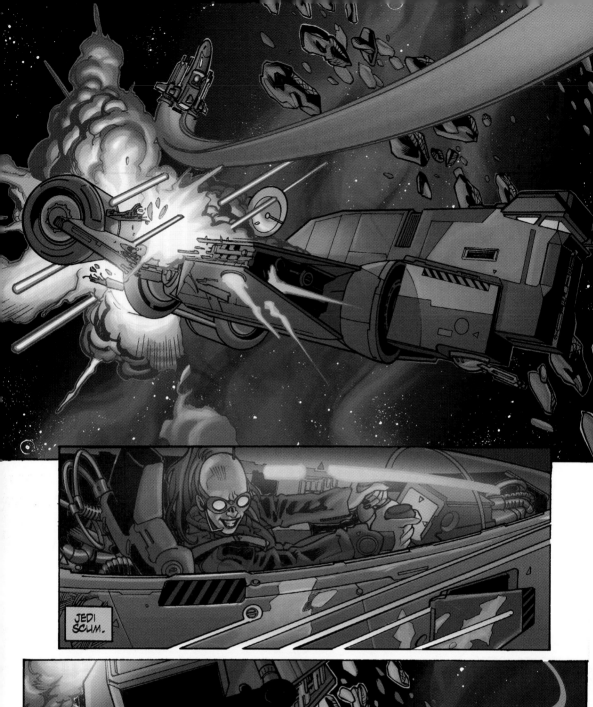

JEDI SCUM.

MASTERS! COMPLETE SYSTEMS FAILURE! ALL SHIELDS DOWN! ONE ENGINE IS GONE, THE OTHER TWO ARE COMPLETELY INOPERABLE!

SHE'S LEAVING! SHE THINKS WE'RE DEAD!

WE MIGHT BE YET! HOLD ON!

THAT WAS CLOSE! SHE ALMOST HAD US!

YES. SHE'S GOOD. VERY GOOD.

IN ANY CASE, SHE DID HER JOB!

THE COMLINK AND THRUSTERS ARE OUT. UNLESS SOMEONE PICKS UP OUR DISTRESS BEACON, WE'LL DRIFT UNTIL THE AIR RUNS OUT.

MAYBE NOT, MASTERS.

SING IS GONE-- BUT ANOTHER SHIP IS APPROACHING!

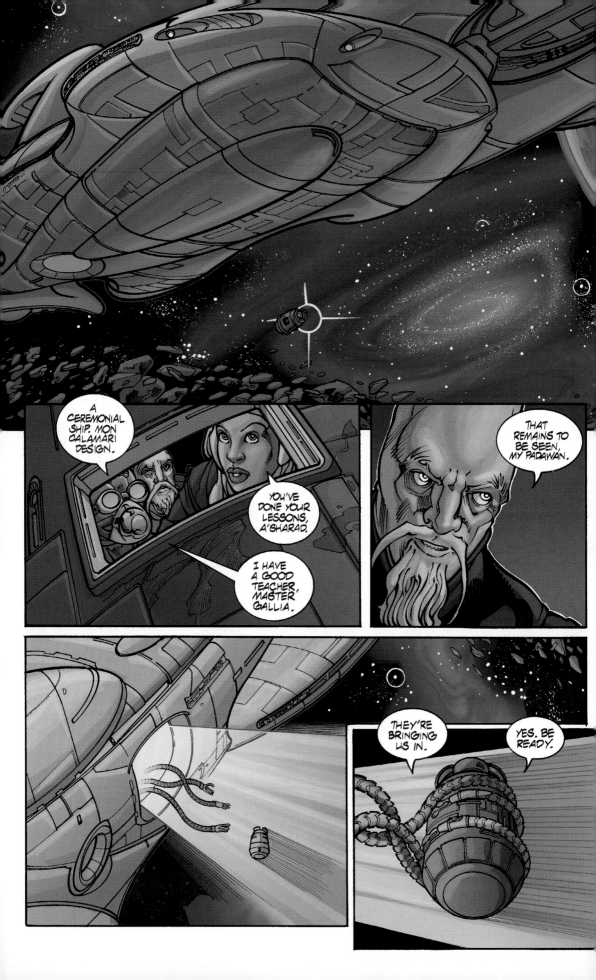

QUARRENS!

SO I SEE.

QUARREN SOLDIERS OF MON CALAMARI, LOWER YOUR WEAPONS. WE ARE ON OFFICIAL BUSINESS BY ORDER OF THE HIGH COUNCIL AND THE JUDICIARY.

SENATOR! THEY ARE JEDI!

BAH! RAGAMUFFIN MAGICIANS! THEY ARE A BOTHER!

WHAT'S THE MEANING OF THIS? I AM *SENATOR TIKKES!* I HAVE URGENT BUSINESS IN THIS SECTOR, AND YOUR INTRUSION HAS COST ME PRECIOUS TIME.

IT WAS CERTAINLY NOT *OUR* WISH TO INTERRUPT YOUR PASSAGE, SENATOR TIKKES.

YOU HAVE EARNED THE GRATITUDE OF THE ENTIRE JEDI COUNCIL.

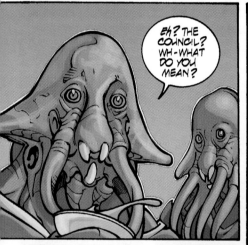

EH? THE COUNCIL? WH-WHAT DO YOU MEAN?

I AM *ADI GALLIA* AND THIS IS *KI-ADI-MUNDI.* WE ARE MEMBERS OF THE JEDI *HIGH COUNCIL.*

THIS IS MASTER KI'S *PADAWAN, A'SHARAD HETT,* SON OF *SHARAD HETT.*

SHARAD HETT? THE FAMOUS JEDI HERO?

I--I AM HONORED! PLEASE... ACCEPT THE MOST GRACIOUS HOSPITALITY OF YOUR FORTUNATE HOST!

I HAD NO IDEA THAT YOU WERE *MEMBERS* OF THE *COUNCIL!*

SHOULD THAT HAVE MATTERED? WE WERE CLEARLY IN DISTRESS. BY REPUBLIC LAW, IT WAS YOUR DUTY TO INTERVENE.

AND INTERVENE HE DID, FRIEND ADI GALLIA. FOR THAT, HE DESERVES OUR MOST SINCERE GRATITUDE.

WE ARE FAR FROM MON CALAMARI, SENATOR. MIGHT I ASK WHAT OFFICIAL BUSINESS BRINGS YOU TO THIS WAYWARD SECTOR?

UH, WELL, IT'S A *BUSINESS* TRIP, ACTUALLY. I HAVE BEEN EYEING CERTAIN UNCLAIMED *INVESTMENT PROPERTIES* IN THESE TERRITORIES. I'VE COME TO INSPECT THEM FIRST HAND.

ALL FOR THE GOOD OF MY CONSTITUENTS AND THE REPUBLIC, I ASSURE YOU.

I'M SURE.

I WON'T BORE YOU WITH DETAILS. YOU HAVE BEEN THROUGH AN EXCRUCIATING ORDEAL!

COME! MY ATTENDANTS SHALL MAKE READY THE FINEST ROOMS ON THIS CRAFT! I'LL INSTRUCT THE PILOTS TO CHANGE OUR COURSE AND TAKE YOU TO THE NEAREST JEDI OUTPOST!

NO NEED FOR THAT. WE SHALL ACCOMPANY YOU, AND YOU CAN DELIVER US ON YOUR RETURN HOME.

B-BUT...

HOW MANY YEARS HAS THIS PLANET BEEN MY ONE HAVEN-- MY ONE SAFE REFUGE--FROM THE RIGORS OF MY JEDI LIFE?

A REFUGEE FROM LIFE-- BUT NOT FROM MEMORY.

THE MEMORY OF MY FAILURE.

THE MEMORY OF THE BEAST WHOM I UNKNOWINGLY UNLEASHED UPON THIS EXISTENCE.

THE ASSASSIN. THE SLAYER OF JEDI.

AURRA SING.

WHY DID THEY NOT LET ME CHASE HER? WHY DID THEY NOT LET ME MAKE AMENDS?

IF ANYONE KNOWS HER WAYS, IT IS I--

--THE ONE THEY CALL *THE DARK WOMAN.*

SHE WAS SO NEAR.

WHY DO I FEEL SHE IS NEAR ME *NOW?*

A METEOR SHOWER. THE SEASON OF THE SKYFALL HAS COME AGAIN.

SO STRANGE.

THE SPACE-BORN ROCKS TEAR THROUGH THE PLANET'S SURFACE, DESTROYING UNTOLD ACRES OF ANCIENT FOLIAGE.

THE VERY METEORS THAT RAVAGE THESE JUNGLES BRING THE NUTRIENTS THAT IT NEEDS TO GROW.

THE WAYS OF THE FORCE ARE STRANGE-- AND WONDROUS.

I'D BEST SEEK SHELTER.

LET'S HOPE THE *QUARRENS'* INFORMATION WAS CORRECT.

INDEED. IT SEEMS THAT IT WAS.

I SHOULD BE PAYING *THEM.*

I'VE WAITED A LONG TIME FOR THIS.

WERE MY EMPLOYERS CORRECT ABOUT EVERYTHING ELSE?

YES. THERE IT IS. JUST PENETRATING THE ATMOSPHERE.

RIGHT ON TIME.

GOOD. I HATE A LATE FUNERAL.

BETTER GET GOING.

I HAVE FLOWERS TO ARRANGE.

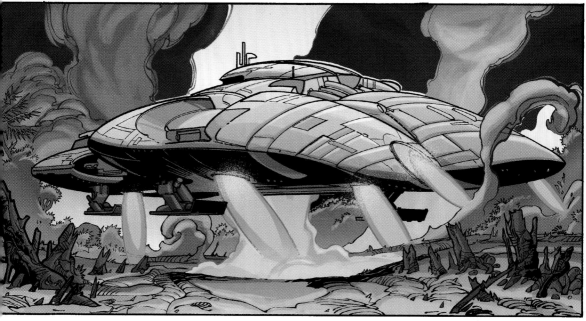

NICE PLACE. WHAT'S HAPPENING OVER THERE?

IMPACT TRAUMA. SENSOR SCAN REVEALED THAT A SEASONAL METEOR STORM OCCURRED JUST BEFORE WE ACHIEVED ORBIT. CLASS 8--A RATHER LARGE ONE.

THE STORMS ARE PART OF THIS PLANET'S NATURAL PROCESS. THESE JUNGLES CONSUME NOURISHMENT AT AN UNIMAGINABLE RATE. THE METEORS RESTORE THE SOIL, BRINGING NUTRIENTS FOR THE NEXT GROWTH CYCLE.

NUTRIENTS.

AND OTHER MINERALS, I SEE.

QUALD RUNIUM, IS IT NOT, MASTER KI?

MY, I HAD NO IDEA THAT THE TUSKEN SAVAGES COULD ACTUALLY BE TRAINED!

QUALD RUNIUM IT IS--IN ITS PURE, UNREFINED FORM!

MY! QUALD RUNIUM, YOU SAY?

WHAT A FORTUNATE-- UH-- COINCIDENCE.

BUT SENATOR, IT'S JUST AS YOUR EXPEDITIONARY TEAMS--*UMPPH!!*

QUIET, TRACTON, LEST YOUR TECHNICAL BABBLE BORE OUR GUESTS! WE'LL SHARE YOUR OBSERVATIONS *LATER!*

IT MAY BE UNWISE FOR YOU TO BE HERE, SENATOR... THIS IS AN UNTAMED PLACE, IN THE MIDST OF A DANGEROUS STORM CYCLE--

MY SCIENTISTS TELL ME THAT THERE WON'T BE ANOTHER STORM UNTIL TOMORROW. BY THEN, I WILL HAVE FINISHED MY EVALUATION.

BESIDES, AS YOU CAN SEE, I'M WELL-PROTECTED.

WELL DONE! NOW, CONTINUE SECURING THE LANDING PERIMETER!

CLEAR A PATH THROUGH THOSE TREES, SO THAT WE CAN SET UP THE MESON DIAGNOSTIC SCANNERS.

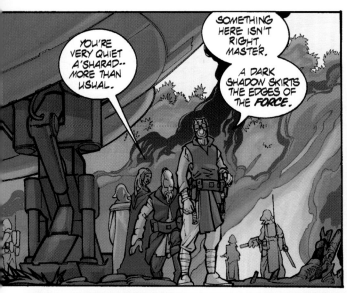

YOU'RE VERY QUIET A'SHARAD-- MORE THAN USUAL.

SOMETHING HERE ISN'T RIGHT, MASTER.

A DARK SHADOW SKIRTS THE EDGES OF THE *FORCE*.

ALL WORLDS ARE FULL OF SHADOWS, MY PADAWAN.

A'SHARAD IS RIGHT, KI. SURELY YOU SENSE IT, TOO?

YES.

STAY CLOSE. IF THERE'S DANGER, WE'LL FACE IT TOGETHER.

<ARR! WHAT HAVE WE HERE??>

< MY LUCKY DAY! >

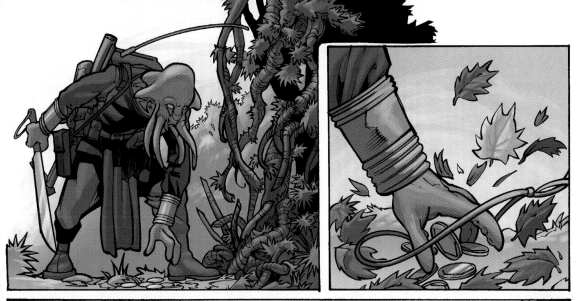

OHHEE

SENATOR!
ONE OF THE
MEN IS IN
TROUBLE!

WELL DON'T JUST
STAND THERE! GO
CUT HIM DOWN AND
MAKE SURE THERE
AREN'T ANY MORE!

NO! WAIT!
SOMETHING
IS WRONG!

TH-
THEY'RE
GONE! ALMOST
ALL OF THEM!
HOW--?

MINES!
SOMEONE
PLANNED
IT THAT
WAY!

IS SHE DEAD?

NOT LIKELY! QUICKLY! GET THE SENATOR AND HIS AIDES INTO THE SHIP!

NO, MASTER! I MUST FIND *AURRA SING*!

YOU *HEARD* ME, PADAWAN! GUARD THE SENATOR! WE HAVE OTHER THINGS TO THINK ABOUT RIGHT NOW!

MY OLD *TEACHER* IS UP THERE IN THOSE HILLS SOMEPLACE--WOUNDED... PERHAPS *DEAD!* I HAVE TO REACH HER!

THAT MEANS THAT *YOU* HAVE TO CHECK ON OUR *ASSASSIN,* MASTER GALLIA.

UNDERSTOOD. BE CAREFUL, KI!

AND YOU AS WELL! THE BEAST IS NOT DEAD--ONLY WAITING!

KI!

FIRST TEACHER?

YES. I COULD *SCARCE* BELIEVE MY EYES WHEN I SAW YOU DOWN THERE! *MANY* SURPRISES TODAY, IT SEEMS.

WHAT BRINGS YOU HERE?

NOT MY OWN WILL, I MUST CONFESS.

THE LIVING HAND OF THE *FORCE* IS AT WORK, THAT IS CERTAIN.

TIKKES' BODYGUARD *SHOT* YOU! WE MUST TEND TO YOUR WOUND.

NO-- THAT'S *NOT* THE IMPORTANT THING! YOU KNOW THAT, KI!

AURRA SING IS DOWN THERE! BOUNTY HUNTER... SLAYER OF *JEDI!*... MY *STUDENT!*

HAS SHE FINALLY COME TO KILL ME?

PERHAPS...

"...HOWEVER, I DON'T THINK YOURS IS THE *ONLY* LIGHTSABER SHE MEANS TO COLLECT THIS DAY.

GONE! WHY AM I NOT SURPRISED?

BUT WHERE?

MY FORCE POWERS TELL ME THAT THIS CASE IS BOOBYTRAPPED. ENOUGH THERMAL EXPLOSIVE TO OBLITERATE A PROVINCE.

WHATEVER IT CONTAINS MUST BE VERY *IMPORTANT* TO HER.

REASON ENOUGH TO SEE WHAT'S INSIDE!

KLIK

SCIENTIST! ARE ALL BOARDING RAMPS AND AIRLOCKS SEALED?

Y-YES, BRAVE PADAWAN! I-I THINK SO. NO ONE CAN ENTER UNLESS WE PERMIT THEM.

SEE? ALL ENTRANCE PORTS AND EMERGENCY EXITS SECURED. ALL SYSTEMS OPERATIONAL. AIR FILTRATION INTAKES ARE RECYCLING OXYGEN FROM THE OUTSIDE. HULL PHOTORECEPTORS AT FULL SCAN--

AIR FILTRATION INTAKES? WHERE?

THERE. NEAR THE ATMOSPHERE CHARGING TURBINES.

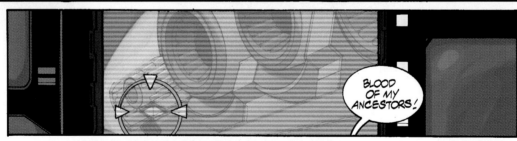

BLOOD OF MY ANCESTORS!

...SHE'S IN!

THAT CREATURE?! I-IN?! IMPOSSIBLE!

AKKHH!

NO. AS YOU CAN SEE, *VERY* POSSIBLE.

SENATOR TIKKES OF MON CALAMARI. ONE OF THE REPUBLIC'S FINE POLITICIANS.

KILLING YOU WILL BE A PUBLIC SERVICE.

FIRST YOU. THEN THE FOOLISH PADAWAN.

THEN HIS FRIENDS OUTSIDE.

WHAT A WONDERFUL DAY THIS TURNED INTO. VERY FULL. VERY REWARDING.

A GIRL COULD GET SPOILED.

I SHALL HAVE *BOTH* THOSE WEAPONS, BOY. BEFORE THIS DAY IS THROUGH.

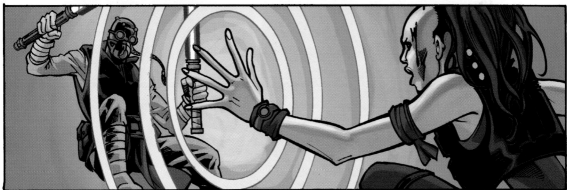

SLAM

A'SHARAD!

YES, MASTER KI. I AM HERE.

YOU DEFEATED HER, PADAWAN HETT! WELL DONE!

WELL DONE, MASTER?

I THINK NOT.

WHAT DO YOU MEAN? WHAT IS THIS DARKNESS I FEEL UPON YOUR HEART?

JUST THAT, MASTER. A DARKNESS, LIKE NOTHING I EVER FELT BEFORE.

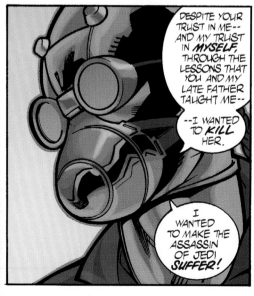

DESPITE YOUR TRUST IN ME-- AND MY TRUST IN MYSELF, THROUGH THE LESSONS THAT YOU AND MY LATE FATHER TAUGHT ME--

--I WANTED TO KILL HER.

I WANTED TO MAKE THE ASSASSIN OF JEDI SUFFER!

I CAN NO LONGER BE YOUR PADAWAN, NOR CAN I TRUST MYSELF TO PURSUE THE WAYS OF THE FORCE.

I ASK TO BE FREED OF MY VOWS TO YOU, AND WILL, IN KIND, FREE YOU OF THE VOW THAT YOU MADE TO MY FATHER.

TAKE ME BACK TO *TATOOINE*... TO MY PEOPLE... TO THE VOICELESS, DEADLY DESERT. THERE, I CAN HARM NO ONE.

WE *ALL* HAVE A DARKNESS WITHIN US, A'SHARAD HETT. IT IS WHAT MAKES US LIVING BEINGS, BOUND BY THE FORCE.

WE CAN NEVER BRUSH THAT DARKNESS AWAY. IT IS WITHIN US ALWAYS.

WE CAN ONLY LEARN TO CONTROL IT, LIKE A DANGEROUS BEAST THAT MUST BE KEPT UPON A CHAIN.

I KNOW OF THIS DARKNESS. I HAVE SEEN THOSE WHO BECOME *LOST* TO IT, LIKE THAT CREATURE DOWN THERE.

PLEASE... STAY WITH THE JEDI. FOR A WHILE, AT LEAST. AND WITH MASTER KI'S PERMISSION, ALLOW *ME* TO BECOME YOUR TEACHER.

ARE YOU SURE OF THIS, FIRST TEACHER?

I AM SURE. I *NEED* THIS BOY, KI. AND HE NEEDS ME.

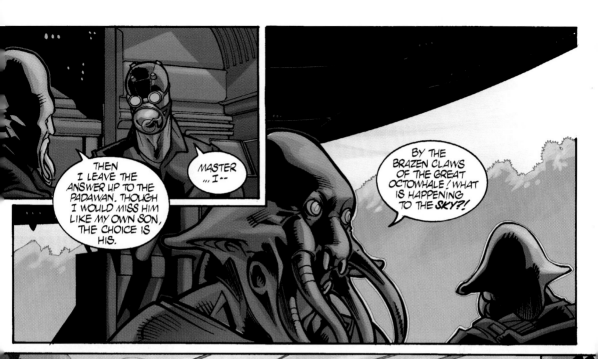

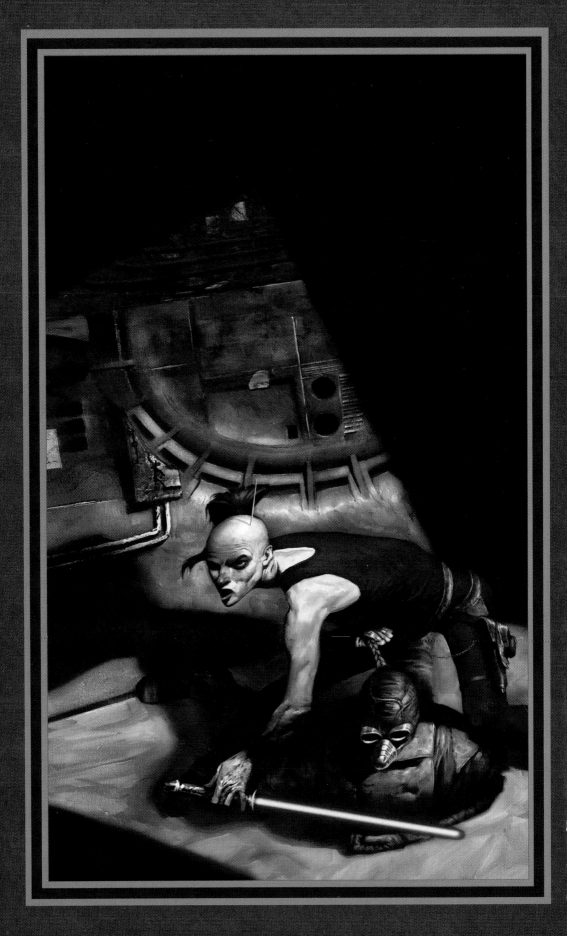